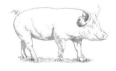
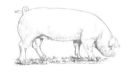

BEAUTIFUL PIGS

JOURNAL

Ivy Press

A PIG SPOTTER'S FIELD GUIDE

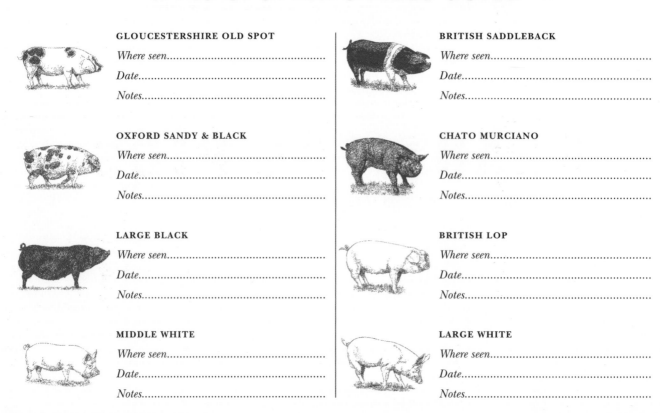

GLOUCESTERSHIRE OLD SPOT

Where seen...

Date...

Notes..

OXFORD SANDY & BLACK

Where seen...

Date...

Notes..

LARGE BLACK

Where seen...

Date...

Notes..

MIDDLE WHITE

Where seen...

Date...

Notes..

BRITISH SADDLEBACK

Where seen...

Date...

Notes..

CHATO MURCIANO

Where seen...

Date...

Notes..

BRITISH LOP

Where seen...

Date...

Notes..

LARGE WHITE

Where seen...

Date...

Notes..

DUROC

Where seen..

Date..

Notes...

WELSH

Where seen..

Date..

Notes...

LANDRACE

Where seen..

Date..

Notes...

AMERICAN LANDRACE

Where seen..

Date..

Notes...

AMERICAN DUROC

Where seen..

Date..

Notes...

POLAND CHINA

Where seen..

Date..

Notes...

SWALLOW-BELLIED MANGALITZA

Where seen..

Date..

Notes...

BLACK VIETNAMESE POT-BELLIED PIG

Where seen..

Date..

Notes...

GLOUCESTERSHIRE OLD SPOT
BOAR

The Gloucestershire Old Spot came to prominence just after the First World War, after the Agriculture Board started the Boar Licensing Scheme. When a herd book was formed, hundreds were exported all over the world. They became so popular that too much poor-quality stock was used for breeding. In 1974 it was classed as endangered.

OXFORD
SANDY & BLACK
SOW

The Oxford Sandy & Black emerged as a distinct breed around 200 years ago. The Oxford is a large, attractive pig, sandy to ginger in colour, covered with black blotches, and with four white feet and a white tip to its tail. Docile and easily managed, it was the cottage dweller's favourite, and was known as the 'Plum Pudding' pig.

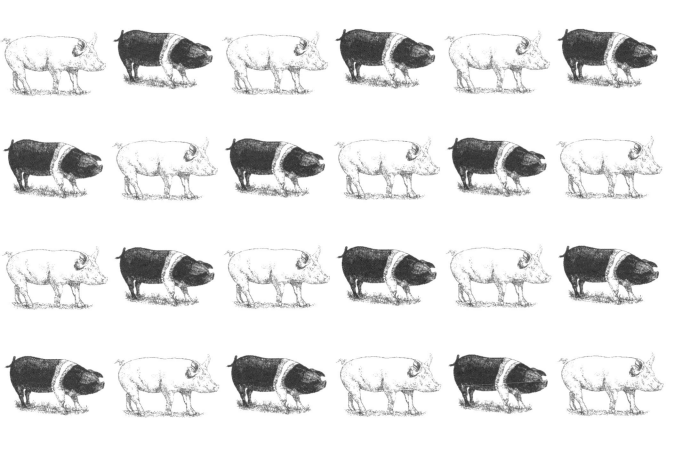

LARGE BLACK
SOW

The modern LARGE BLACK is derived from two black pig varieties. One was a huge beast from Devon and Cornwall and the other, from south-east England, was very long with shorter legs. Some were dirty white with black, and both were prolific and hardy. Neapolitan and perhaps Chinese blood is also presumed to be present.

MIDDLE WHITE
SOW

The MIDDLE WHITE is a sweet-natured, gentle and docile pig. It is of medium size; a heavier type, though smaller than the Large White, it has fine bones and shorter legs. Its Chinese ancestry shows in its short, dished face and snub nose and tubby appearance. It needs protection from excessive heat and sunshine and extremes of cold.

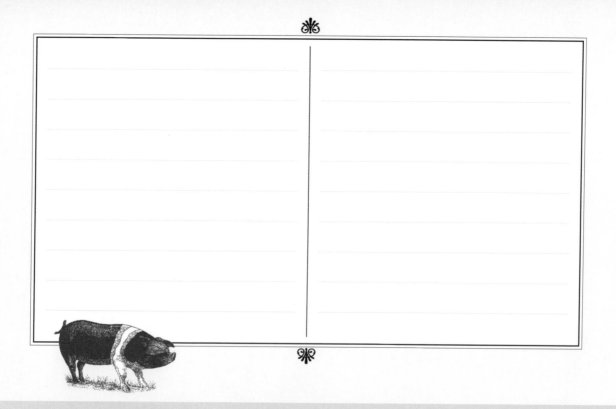

BRITISH SADDLEBACK
SOW

In the seventeenth century, black pigs were favoured in southern England. When Neapolitan and Siamese pigs were used to improve type and succulence, then crossed with the banded New Forest pig, black-and-white pigs were produced. The BRITISH SADDLEBACK had a white belly band that went over the front legs and shoulders.

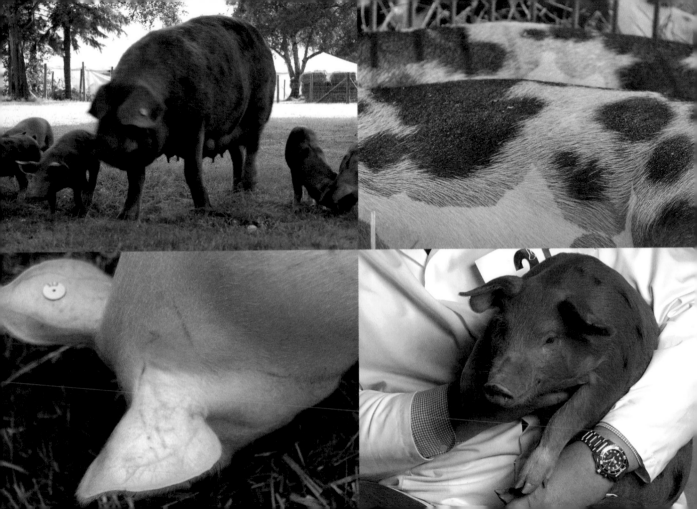

CHATO MURCIANO
SOW

The delightful, slate-grey Chato Murciano has a very old Spanish ancestry, hailing from south-eastern Murcia. In 1865 there were 50,000 of them and more than twice as many in 1929. It is thrifty, hardy and easily managed, doing well on farm by-products and waste food; consequently it is suited to many systems of pig keeping.

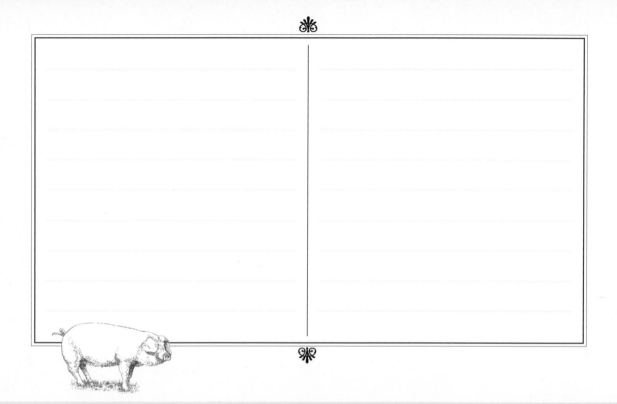

BRITISH LOP
SOW

These large, long pigs came from the old, white Celtic pigs of Ireland and Wales. They are popular with farmers in the West Country, the pigs being docile, self-sufficient, hardy and good grazers and foragers. The BRITISH LOP produces excellent pork and bacon. The breed society, formed in 1918, keep their own independent herd book.

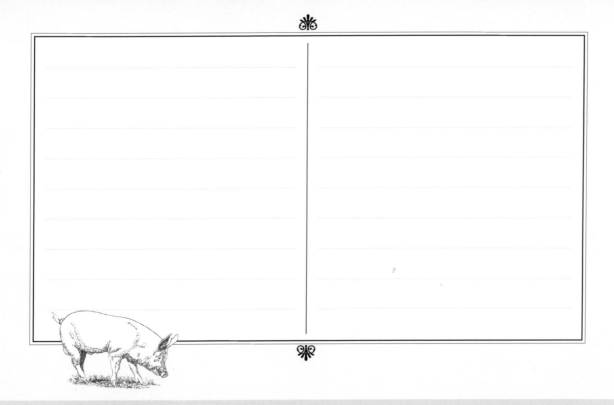

LARGE WHITE
SOW

The Large White or Yorkshire is probably the most popular pig in the world. They consistently have litters of 10–12 and always milk well. Butchers like them because they produce large, meaty porkers and their bacon is legendary for its texture and flavour. In its early history it had big lop ears on a long head; it was improved by selective breeding.

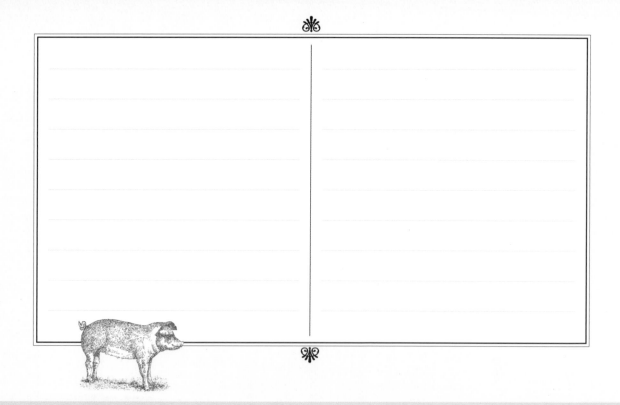

DUROC
SOW

The British Duroc was imported from the USA during the 1950s and 1960s by the large commercial pig-breeding companies to use in their breeding programmes. It wasn't until the 1990s, however, that it became accepted in the UK as a pure breed. The Duroc's weight gain is phenomenal on a fairly meagre diet.

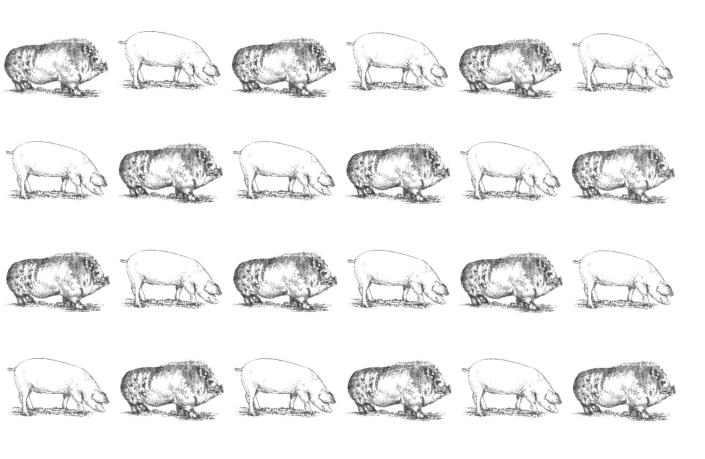

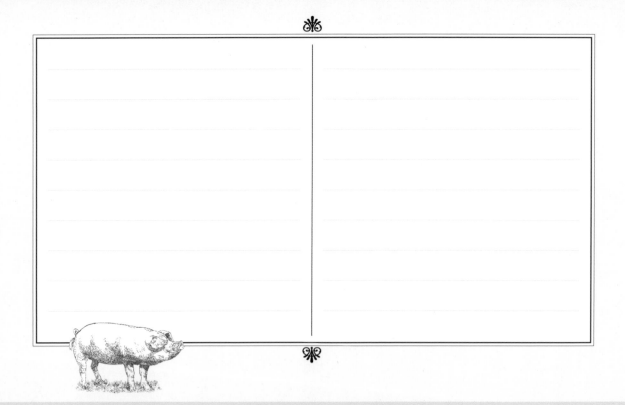

WELSH
SOW

The WELSH pig came from unpromising beginnings. It was described in the nineteenth century as a razor-backed, coarse-haired, slow-maturing type with very long legs, but the modern pig bears no resemblance to this description. It has become very successful, not unlike the Landrace but with the dish face of the Large White and a long back.

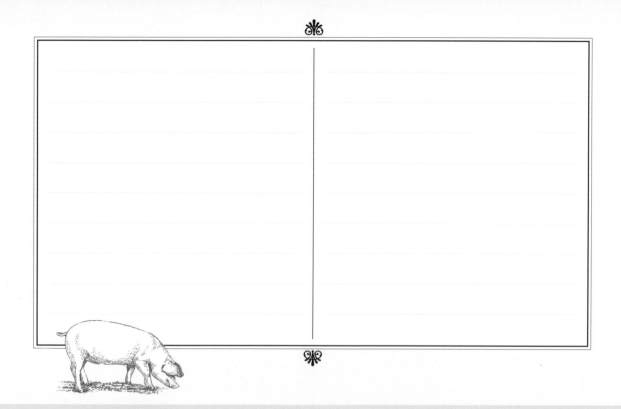

LANDRACE
SOW

The LANDRACE is a Danish export, arriving in Britain in 1949. It is a cross between two original Celtic land pigs of Denmark, with Chinese, Iberian and English breeds such as the Middle White and Berkshire. To improve the pigs' production of bacon, they were then crossed with the Large White in the last quarter of the nineteenth century.

AMERICAN LANDRACE
SOW

The long-bodied, white Landrace pig was developed in Denmark and registered in 1906. The breed arrived in America in 1934 and was followed by the Norwegian Landrace in 1954. Both were crossed with indigenous American breeds and to date over 700,000 AMERICAN LANDRACE offspring have been recorded.

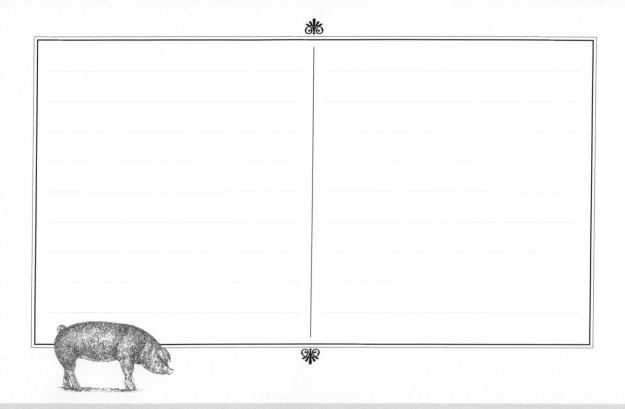

AMERICAN DUROC
SOW

The AMERICAN DUROC is smaller than the Jersey Red that it was originally crossbred with in the early nineteenth century, and it has a better carcass and finer frame. The modern Duroc has an exceptional daily live-weight gain and very good food conversion, making it a particularly good meat pig.

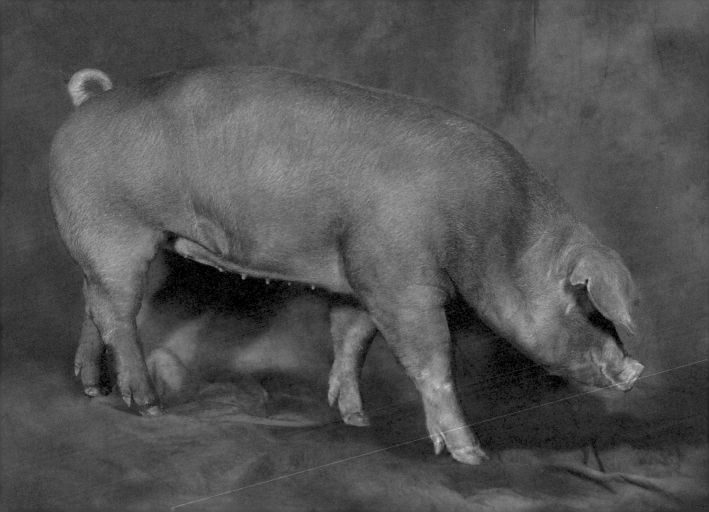

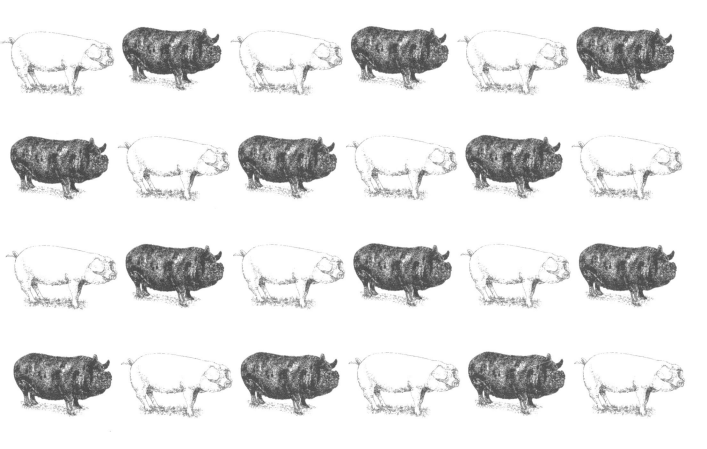

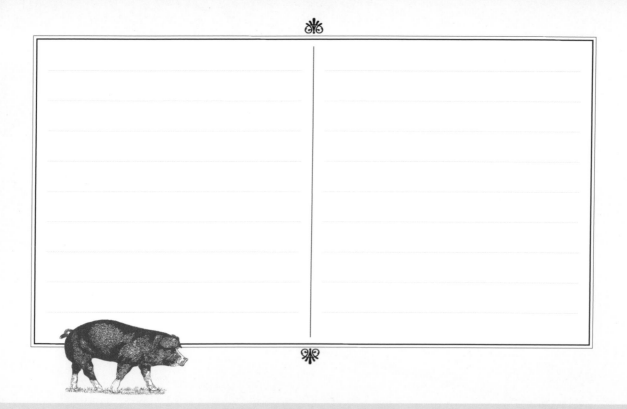

POLAND CHINA
SOW

In 1816 some Big China pigs were taken from Philadelphia to Warren County, Ohio, to improve the indigenous pigs there. The Irish Grazier pig, with its full hams and loins, was bred with Warren County pigs and by 1860 the result was the POLAND CHINA, a large, long-backed coarse pig. The Poland China has become one of the best lean-meat pigs.

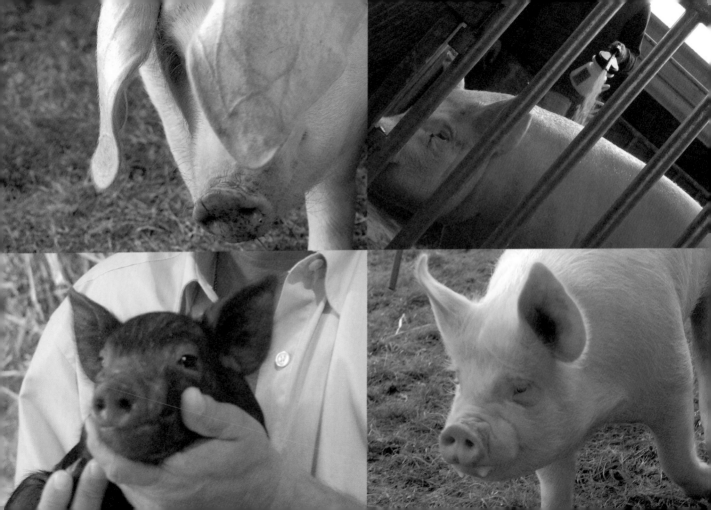

SWALLOW-BELLIED
MANGALITZA
SOW

The Swallow-bellied Mangalitza is believed to have been created by crossing the so-called Black or Slate Grey pig with the Black Syrmian in the south of Hungary. This gave us the slate-grey back and body of this woolly pig with its characteristic fair-coloured underbelly. By selective breeding the colour was fixed.

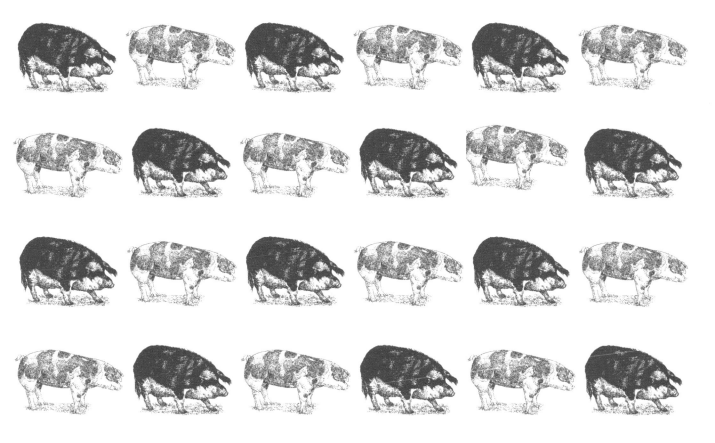